HOPE GARDEN

*Prompts and Encouragements to Cultivate Hope, A
Devotional Study Journal*

MICHAEL LACEY

Story Builds

CREATIVE

Story Builds Creative
2680 Baptist Road, Nesbit, MS 38651
Story-Builds.com

ISBN (digital): 978-0-9998725-5-0
ISBN (paperback): 978-0-9998725-6-7

All production by Michael Lacey with Story Builds Creative.

CONTENTS

Introduction

If you got this as an ebook but would like a printable version, you can get it at MichaelLacey.me/hopegarden.

Hope isn't something you will into existence. It is something that is produced in a well-tended garden, one that flourishes with the constant presence of gratitude, praise and worship, wisdom from God, time in His Word, prayer, and reflection. True growth in the Christian faith requires these things, and they don't only produce hope. They bring you closer to the source of all good things, closer to God Himself.

This study journal is broken down with a completed entry at the beginning of each part to be used as an example. Do not feel pressure to create a super deep bible study with each entry. Just fill them out with your present self. Use this study journal however you feel led, and have fun with it.

If you have the print version, draw in the margins, doodle in empty spaces, add your own flair. When it's full, get another or start a similar one in a blank journal. There are extra journaling pages at the end as well to use however you'd like. These also make great gifts for other women in your life.

How to use this study journal:

- make time for it daily or weekly
- "slow and steady" is the name of this game
- carry it proudly with your copy of Hope When it Hurts: The Scars that Shape Us or As We Fight: A Weekly Guide Through the Warfare of Worship
- for kindling to keep your fire going (figuratively)

How not to use this journal:

- beat yourself up for not being consistent
- lose hope when you don't see progress
- use this as a replacement for your bible reading
- for kindling to keep your fire going (literally, if you have the paperback)

ENTRY FLOW

Each Part starts with an excerpt from Michael's writing "The Garden of Hope" entry from the book that inspired this journal, *Hope When it Hurts: The Scars that Shape Us.*

The first devo of each Part is a sample "tending devo" to get you started. After that, you can use the created templates to plant and water your garden. This can be used one month at a time or at whatever pace works for you. However, remember that it takes daily care for healthy growth, in whatever way it takes to make that happen.

GRATITUDE

In each entry, you'll start with gratitude. This is the foundation for each of the other steps. Recognizing what God has done for you helps frame your perspective of Him and His true goodness.

Praise/Worship

The natural response when we truly see God's workings is praise and worship. While each of those concepts can stand alone, they will be used in conjunction throughout this journal.

As a worship leader myself, I keep an updated list of worship songs that are meaningful to me, including some that are referenced in this book. You can follow that list and listen along on Spotify; go to MichaelLacey.me/hopegarden to get the link. Also, the song titles are links to Youtube videos.

Wisdom/study

This includes a thought to ponder, a verse on which to ruminate, or a teaching from a spiritual authority. These are meant to challenge your preconceived notions of God, who He is, and why He allows the things He does.

Some of these sections will require you to dig for the truth yourself, as I hope you are doing anyways.

Many of the verses are linked to the full chapters on Bible Gateway. Feel free to click on them and read them in context.

Prayer

While this is the last section of each entry, it should not be the end of your time with God but rather a continuation. Philippians tells us to pray without ceasing. Jesus prayed up to the cross and while on it.

May this journal give you the opportunity to cultivate hope, grow closer to God, and live a life that honors Him.

Godspeed,
-Michael Lacey, Story-Builds.com | ChristWriters.com

PART I

Do you need a prescription for hope? Not as in, "I'm suffering from hope, please help me." Nobody would say something like that. Well, maybe some of us hopeless romantics, but that's another story.

I won't leave you hanging. There is one thing you must do to increase your hope: worship.

Praise is the prescription for hope. The garden of hope requires praise foremost, then as consequence of praise: grace, wisdom, faith, and proper perspectives.

Firstly, let us acknowledge this truth:

> "As Christ's kingdom is not of this world, so is not our hope. The worldling's motto is, "a bird in the hand." Give me today, say they, and take tomorrow whoso will. But the word of believers is, spero meliora—my hopes are better than my present possessions."

-Elnathan Parr

I'll warn you up front. This particular devotional story will be filled with incredible quotes and writings from great people of God. I'm simply delivering the words the Holy Spirit has inspired me to hold onto lately. To find hope, learn how to praise. To learn how to praise, go to the Psalms and their incredible depth and insight.

In the Treasury of David Psalm study, Charles Spurgeon says of Psalm 27,

> *"It is a song of cheerful hope, well fitted for those in trial who have learned to lean upon the Almighty arm."*

How is praise supposed to build hope? Well, it builds more than just hope. Hope becomes a byproduct, or perhaps even a fruit, of well-placed praise.

We know this: God desires to be known, to be worshiped. Through reading His word, praying to Him, praising, and worshiping, we know more of Him and His attributes, His qualities. In knowing Him more, we trust Him more. In all of those things, we see His faithfulness. And in knowing He is faithful, we grow in faith. At some point, we can't help but hope, because we begin to know what waits on the other side of each trial, each storm, each hardship.

God waits on the other side with open arms. He stands next to us hand-in-hand, and He goes before us with His mighty right hand.

1 | God's Goodness

Today, I am grateful for a God who is truly good. There is no malice in Him toward His children. He loves me, and He desires a full and present life for me with Him. I am also grateful for people in my life who worship faithfully. They are a great example for me and many others. I want to be like that, one after God's heart.

Praise/Worship

I love You, Lord for Your mercy never fails me
All my days, I've been held in Your hands
From the moment that I wake up until I lay my head
Oh, I will sing of the goodness of God
And all my life You have been faithful
And all my life You have been so, so good
With every breath that I am able
Oh, I will sing of the goodness of God
I love Your voice, You have led me through the fire
In the darkest night You are close like no other
I've known You as a Father
I've known You as a Friend
And I have lived in the goodness of God
-Goodness of God[1]

Oh, give thanks to the Lord! Call upon His name;

Make known His deeds among the peoples!

Sing to Him, sing psalms to Him;

Talk of all His wondrous works!

Glory in His holy name;

Let the hearts of those rejoice who seek the Lord!

Seek the Lord and His strength; Seek His face evermore!

Remember His marvelous works which He has done,

His wonders, and the judgments of His mouth,

O seed of Abraham His servant,

You children of Jacob, His chosen ones!

-Psalm 105:1-6 (NKJV)

Prayer

God, help me to see the beautiful things in my life and recognize that it is all from You. In response to that, I will praise you, not just in this moment but throughout this day and with my life. As Romans 12:1 says, I offer my life as a living sacrifice, holy and pleasing to You; this will be my true worship.

Journal

Feel free to continue journaling any thoughts you have about God, His goodness, and what He has given you.

God_____

GRATITUDE

Today, I am thankful for:

_____

_____

_____

_____

PRAISE/WORSHIP

Remember a worship song or phrase from your memory and sing it to God without using your voice. Do this from your soul in worship to the King. You can write some lyrics here:

_____

_____

_____

_____

WISDOM/STUDY

Write a verse or teaching you've recently heard that is sparking in your soul:

_____

_____

_____

_____

Prayer

Writing out our prayers gives them more intention, but it's not necessary. Do as you feel led to:

_____

_____

_____

_____

_____

Journal

_____

_____

_____

_____

_____

_____

_____

_____

_____

_____

_____

_____

_____

_____

_____

_____

_____

_____

God_____

Gratitude

_____

_____

_____

_____

_____

_____

Praise/Worship

_____

_____

_____

_____

_____

_____

Wisdom/study

_____

_____

_____

_____

_____

_____

Prayer

_____

_____

_____

_____

_____

_____

Journal

God_____

GRATITUDE

_____

_____

_____

_____

_____

_____

PRAISE/WORSHIP

_____

_____

_____

_____

_____

_____

WISDOM/STUDY

_____

_____

_____

_____

_____

_____

PRAYER

_____

_____

_____

_____

_____

_____

Journal

God_____

GRATITUDE

_____

_____

_____

_____

_____

_____

PRAISE/WORSHIP

_____

_____

_____

_____

_____

_____

WISDOM/STUDY

_____

_____

_____

_____

_____

_____

PRAYER

_____

_____

_____

_____

_____

_____

Journal

God_____

GRATITUDE

_____
_____
_____
_____
_____
_____

PRAISE/WORSHIP

_____
_____
_____
_____
_____
_____

WISDOM/STUDY

_____
_____
_____
_____
_____
_____

PRAYER

_____
_____
_____
_____
_____
_____

God_____

GRATITUDE

_____
_____
_____
_____
_____
_____

PRAISE/WORSHIP

_____
_____
_____
_____
_____
_____

WISDOM/STUDY

_____
_____
_____
_____
_____
_____

PRAYER

_____
_____
_____
_____
_____
_____

Journal

PART II

Storms are not timid, they are not tame, and they do not care who they affect. However, our God is not timid, He is certainly not tame, but He does care. William S. Plumer wrote, ***"Hope in God. The more terrible the storm, the more necessary is the anchor."***

> "We have this hope as an anchor for the soul, firm and secure."
>
> Hebrews 6:19a (CSB)

These men knew something about hope that often alludes so many of us. Let's go deeper.

> "Why am I agitated like a troubled sea, and why do my thoughts make a noise like a tumultuous multitude? The causes are not enough to justify such utter yielding to despondency. Up, my heart! . . . ***Hope*** thou in God. If every evil be let loose from Pandora's box, yet is there ***hope*** at the bottom." -Spurgeon

In Psalms 42:5 and 43:5, the word "disquieted" is more literally "tumultuated," as in the tossing of the roaring, tumultuous sea.

> "Why are you cast down, O my soul? And why are you disquieted within me? Hope in God, for I shall yet praise Him for the help of His countenance."
>
> -Psalm 42:5; 43:5 (NKJV)

When we read this verse, we don't think of our sorrows. We grow in hope. Our hope lays sorrow's assertions and arguments to rest. Faith disproves fears rebuttals.

> "Even though I walk through the valley of the shadow of death, I fear no evil, for You are with me; Your rod and Your staff, they comfort me."
>
> -Psalm 23:4 (NASB)

When we read this chapter, we don't think about the valley of the shadow of death, we think about the Good Shepherd who is with us, always has been, and always will be, as He leads us along the right paths.

> "You intended to harm me, but God intended it for good to accomplish what is now being done, the saving of many lives."
>
> -Genesis 50:20 (NIV)

When we read this passage, we're reminded that God works even the most dire circumstances for our good.

-Michael Lacey, from "The Garden of Hope" writing in the book, *Hope When it Hurts: The Scars that Shape Us*.

8 | God's Sovereignty

Today, I am grateful for breath in my lungs. I want to use that same breath as praise to God. I'm grateful for a God who, even though He holds the universe, holds me as well. He is in heaven, doing as He pleases, yet He is with me. This means it pleases Him to love me, to hold me now.

PRAISE/WORSHIP

Hold me now
In the hands that created the heavens
Find me now
Where the grace runs as deep as Your scars
You pulled me from the clay You set me on a rock
Called me by Your Name
And made my heart whole again
Lifted up and my knees know it's all for Your glory
I might stand with more reasons to sing than to fear
So here I stand high in surrender
I need You now hold my heart
Now and forever my soul cries out
Once I was broken
But You loved my whole heart through

Sin has no hold on me 'cause Your grace holds me now
And that grace owns the ground where the grave did
Where all my shame
Remains left for dead in Your wake
You crashed those age-old gates
You left no stone unturned
You stepped out of that grave
And shouldered me all the way

Healed and forgiven, look where my chains are now
Death has no hold on me
'Cause Your grace holds that ground
And Your grace holds me now

-Whole Heart (Hold Me Now) [1]

Wisdom/study

Not unto us, O Lord, not unto us,

but to Your name give glory,

Because of Your mercy, Because of Your truth.

Why should the Gentiles say, "So where *is* their God?"

But our God *is* in heaven; He does whatever He pleases.

-Psalms 115:1-3 (NKJV)

Prayer

God, I recognize Your sovereignty. I know that You are in heaven and do as You please. I am no one to tell You what should be done. Help me to trust that You have better plans for my life than I ever could.

Journal

Feel free to continue journaling any thoughts you have about God, His sovereignty, and why He may have let you go through some of the difficult things you've experienced.

_____

_____

_____

_____

_____

_____

_____

_____

_____

_____

_____

_____

_____

_____

_____

_____

_____

_____

_____

_____

_____

_____

_____

_____

God_____

Gratitude

_____
_____
_____
_____
_____
_____

Praise/Worship

_____
_____
_____
_____
_____
_____

Wisdom/study

_____
_____
_____
_____
_____
_____

Prayer

_____
_____
_____
_____
_____
_____

Journal

God_____

GRATITUDE

_____
_____
_____
_____
_____
_____

PRAISE/WORSHIP

_____
_____
_____
_____
_____
_____

WISDOM/STUDY

_____
_____
_____
_____
_____
_____

PRAYER

_____
_____
_____
_____
_____
_____

Journal

God_____

Gratitude

_____

Praise/Worship

_____

Wisdom/study

_____

Prayer

_____

Journal

God_____

GRATITUDE

_____

_____

_____

_____

_____

_____

PRAISE/WORSHIP

_____

_____

_____

_____

_____

_____

WISDOM/STUDY

_____

_____

_____

_____

_____

_____

PRAYER

_____

_____

_____

_____

_____

_____

Journal

God_____

Gratitude

_____
_____
_____
_____
_____
_____

Praise/Worship

_____
_____
_____
_____
_____
_____

Wisdom/study

_____
_____
_____
_____
_____
_____

Prayer

_____
_____
_____
_____
_____
_____

JOURNAL

God_____

GRATITUDE

_____
_____
_____
_____
_____
_____

PRAISE/WORSHIP

_____
_____
_____
_____
_____
_____

WISDOM/STUDY

_____
_____
_____
_____
_____
_____

PRAYER

_____
_____
_____
_____
_____
_____

JOURNAL

PART III

❧

It is the darkness, the difficulty, the despair the drive us a God who pours hope out like He does His grace. And it is his grace that becomes the foundation for unshakable hope. Through praise, we recognize His grace. Through grace, we see through the world's economy to something much greater. By grace, we walk with hope.

Once again, Spurgeon's words in his study of Psalm 42:5 honor God and shed light:

> *"This is the grace that swims, though the waves roar*
> *and be troubled. God is unchangeable, and*
> *therefore his grace is the ground for unshaken*
> *hope. If everything be dark, yet the day will come,*
> *and meanwhile* **hope carries stars in her**
> **eyes;** *her lamps are not dependent on oil from*
> *without, her light is fed by secret visitations of*
> *God, which sustain the spirit.*
> **For I shall yet praise him**. *Yet will my sighs give*
> *place to songs, my mournful ditties shall be*
> *exchanged for triumphal paeans. A loss of the*

present sense of God's love is not a loss of that love itself; the jewel is there, though it gleams not on our breast; **hope** knows her title good when she cannot read it clear; she expects the promised boon though present providence stands before her with empty hands.

For I shall yet praise him for the help of his countenance. Salvations come from the propitious face of God, and he will yet lift up his countenance upon us. Note well that the main **hope** and chief desire of David rest in the smile of God. His face is what he seeks and **hopes** to see, and this will recover his low spirits, this will put to scorn his laughing enemies, this will restore to him all the joys of those holy and happy days around which memory lingers. This is grand cheer. This verse, like the singing of Paul and Silas, looses chains and shakes prison walls. He who can use such heroic language in his gloomy hours will surely conquer. In the garden of **hope** grow the laurels for future victories, the roses of coming joy, the lilies of approaching peace...

Wherefore indulge unreasonable sorrows, which benefit no one, fret thyself, and dishonour thy God? Why overburden thyself with forebodings? **Hope** in God, or wait for God. There is need of patience, but there is ground for **hope**. The Lord cannot but avenge his own elect. The heavenly Father will not stand by and see his children trampled on for ever; as surely as the sun is in the heavens, light must arise for the people of God, though for awhile they may walk in darkness. Why, then, should we not be encouraged, and lift up our head with comfortable hope?

For I shall yet praise him. *Times of complaint will soon end, and seasons of praise will begin. Come, my heart, look out of the window, borrow the telescopic glass, forecast a little, and sweeten thy chamber with sprigs of the sweet herb of* **hope**. *Who is the health of my countenance, and my God. My God will clear the furrows from my brow, and the tear marks from my cheek; therefore will I lift up my head and smile in the face of the storm."*

15 | God Behind the Scenes

Gratitude

Today, I am grateful for a God who works in the background as well as in front, for knowing better than me, for having ways and thoughts that are higher than mine. I'm also thankful for the wisdom God is giving me now as well as the insight into my soul and His workings.

Praise/Worship

Here's a great bridge from a powerful worship song. Recite this chorus and bridge today as you go throughout your day. Do it at least once right now.

> *Even when I don't see it, You're working.*
> *Even when I don't feel it, You're working.*
> *You never stop, You never stop working.*
> *You never stop, You never stop working.*
> *Way Maker,*
> *Miracle worker,*
> *Promise keeper,*
> *Light in the darkness.*
> *My God, that is who You are.*
>
> *-Waymaker* [1]

We know that all things work together for the good of those who love God, who are called according to His purpose.

-Romans 8:28 (CSB)

"For my thoughts are not your thoughts,

and your ways are not my ways." This is the Lord's declaration.

"For as heaven is higher than earth, so my ways are higher than your ways, and my thoughts than your thoughts."

-Isaiah 55:8-9 (CSB)

Prayer

God, even when I don't see it, I know, I trust that You are working. Grow my faith through times like these. Protect me from the lies of the enemy, and give me the ears to hear Your voice over all others.

Journal

Continue journaling about a time when God was working but you didn't see it until later. If you feel you are in the middle of one of those times, talk to God about it. Write it.

God_____

Gratitude

_____
_____
_____
_____
_____
_____

Praise/Worship

_____
_____
_____
_____
_____
_____

Wisdom/study

_____
_____
_____
_____
_____
_____

Prayer

_____
_____
_____
_____
_____
_____

JOURNAL

God_____

Gratitude

_____
_____
_____
_____
_____
_____

Praise/Worship

_____
_____
_____
_____
_____
_____

Wisdom/study

_____
_____
_____
_____
_____
_____

Prayer

_____
_____
_____
_____
_____
_____

Journal

God_____

GRATITUDE

_____
_____
_____
_____
_____
_____

PRAISE/WORSHIP

_____
_____
_____
_____
_____
_____

WISDOM/STUDY

_____
_____
_____
_____
_____
_____

PRAYER

_____
_____
_____
_____
_____
_____

Journal

God_____

Gratitude

_____
_____
_____
_____
_____
_____

Praise/Worship

_____
_____
_____
_____
_____
_____

Wisdom/study

_____
_____
_____
_____
_____
_____

Prayer

_____
_____
_____
_____
_____
_____

JOURNAL

God_____

Gratitude

_____
_____
_____
_____
_____
_____

Praise/Worship

_____
_____
_____
_____
_____
_____

Wisdom/study

_____
_____
_____
_____
_____
_____

Prayer

_____
_____
_____
_____
_____
_____

Journal

God_____

Gratitude

_____
_____
_____
_____
_____
_____

Praise/Worship

_____
_____
_____
_____
_____
_____

Wisdom/study

_____
_____
_____
_____
_____
_____

Prayer

_____
_____
_____
_____
_____
_____

JOURNAL

PART IV

One of the tenets of worship—and the Christian life— is to get outside of ourselves. When we fix our eyes on Jesus, the things of this world fade away. When we strive to be like Him, we begin to seek out ways to serve rather than to be served. Erwin McManus, in his devotional from The Way of the Warrior, writes beautifully about this shift as he equates selflessness to wisdom and wisdom to hope.

"The warrior wields a weapon only to defend, protect,
and liberate. When the warrior is wise, they fight
only for peace.
Where there is wisdom, there is always hope. Wisdom
simplifies. Wisdom clarifies. Wisdom untangles.
Wisdom unshackles. Wisdom illuminates...This is
the highest expression of wisdom—to live our lives
for others rather than ourselves...
It is a small thing to simply fight for yourself when
there are so many who need your battle cry...
What is done for ourselves will one day be forgotten,
but that what we have done for others will be
remembered for eternity."

Let us look not in or even around, not at first. Let us look up, to God who is in the heavens and does as He pleases (Psalm 115:3). Let us praise the Maker, the Creator, the Majestic. As we focus on Him, our priorities step in line. As we look to the King, our reverence deepens. As we acknowledge the goodness and power of God, our faith grows. As we grow to know Him more, we walk in wisdom, in grace, and by His nature, in hope.

Tend the garden with praise, and don't be overwhelmed when you begin to hope for things immeasurable and beyond the scope of your imagination.

22 | God My Warrior King

GRATITUDE

Today, I am grateful for a God who fights for me! I'm thankful for the Christian life, the promise that God is for us, and the fact that the enemy has already lost. I'm also grateful for the victories in my life, both from my obedience to God and His faithfulness.

PRAISE/WORSHIP

Worship is warfare. We fight our battles with worship. Such battles are the collision of God's will, man's will, and the enemy's will, each one demanding worship in one way or another. We know that only One is truly worthy of it. Fight your battles today by worshiping and letting God fight for you.

> *This is how I fight my battles*
> *It may look like I'm surrounded*
> *But I'm surrounded by You*
> *-Surrounded (Fight My Battles)[1]*

> *I raise a hallelujah, in the presence of my enemies*
> *I raise a hallelujah, louder than the unbelief*
> *I raise a hallelujah, my weapon is a melody*
> *I raise a hallelujah, heaven comes to fight for me*
> *I'm gonna sing, in the middle of the storm*

Louder and louder, you're gonna hear my praises roar
Up from the ashes, hope will arise
Death is defeated, the King is alive!
I raise a hallelujah, with everything inside of me
I raise a hallelujah, I will watch the darkness flee
I raise a hallelujah, in the middle of the mystery
I raise a hallelujah, fear you lost your hold on me!
-Raise a Hallelujah [2]

Wisdom/study

In 2 Chronicles, Jehoshaphat feared men that were coming against him for battle. He sought the Lord and followed His command by doing what seemed insane. He sent the singers first into battle.

It may seem like it doesn't make sense sometimes to follow God, but He always knows better. In this account, He's teaching us that as well as the model of worshiping first, worshiping in the midst of the battle.

. . . he appointed those who were to sing to the Lord and praise him in holy attire, as they went before the army, and say, "Give thanks to the Lord for his steadfast love endures forever."

And when they began to sing and praise, the Lord set an ambush against the men of Ammon, Moab, and Mount Seir, who had come against Judah, so that they were routed. For the men of Ammon and Moab rose against the inhabitants of Mount Seir, devoting them to destruction, and when they had made an end of the inhabitants of Seir, they all helped to destroy one another.

-2 Chronicles 20: 21-23 (ESV)

Prayer

God, I do surrender both my will and my mind to You. I trust You to lead me. I will praise you in the rain, in the flood, in the storm. Even when the water surrounds me, I will trust that it is from You and for You. I know You will deliver me in Your perfect timing. God, increase my faith, and give me the courage to let you do so.

Journal

Journal your bold and courageous thoughts right now. Whatever enemy you are facing now, call it out and claim victory in the name of Christ. Worship like your life depends on it, because it does.

_____

_____

_____

_____

_____

_____

_____

_____

_____

_____

_____

_____

_____

_____

_____

_____

_____

_____

God_____

GRATITUDE

_____

_____

_____

_____

_____

_____

PRAISE/WORSHIP

_____

_____

_____

_____

_____

_____

WISDOM/STUDY

_____

_____

_____

_____

_____

_____

PRAYER

_____

_____

_____

_____

_____

_____

Journal

God_____

Gratitude

_____
_____
_____
_____
_____
_____

Praise/Worship

_____
_____
_____
_____
_____
_____

Wisdom/study

_____
_____
_____
_____
_____
_____

Prayer

_____
_____
_____
_____
_____
_____

JOURNAL

God_____

Gratitude

_____
_____
_____
_____
_____
_____

Praise/Worship

_____
_____
_____
_____
_____
_____

Wisdom/study

_____
_____
_____
_____
_____
_____

Prayer

_____
_____
_____
_____
_____
_____

JOURNAL

God_____

Gratitude

_____
_____
_____
_____
_____
_____

Praise/Worship

_____
_____
_____
_____
_____
_____

Wisdom/study

_____
_____
_____
_____
_____
_____

Prayer

_____
_____
_____
_____
_____
_____

JOURNAL

God_____

Gratitude

_____
_____
_____
_____
_____
_____

Praise/Worship

_____
_____
_____
_____
_____
_____

Wisdom/study

_____
_____
_____
_____
_____
_____

Prayer

_____
_____
_____
_____
_____
_____

Journal

God_____

GRATITUDE

_____
_____
_____
_____
_____
_____

PRAISE/WORSHIP

_____
_____
_____
_____
_____
_____

WISDOM/STUDY

_____
_____
_____
_____
_____
_____

PRAYER

_____
_____
_____
_____
_____
_____

JOURNAL

PART V
ADDITIONAL
JOURNALING PAGES

God_____

Gratitude

_____

_____

_____

_____

_____

_____

Praise/Worship

_____

_____

_____

_____

_____

_____

Wisdom/study

_____

_____

_____

_____

_____

_____

Prayer

_____

_____

_____

_____

_____

_____

JOURNAL

God_____

GRATITUDE

_____
_____
_____
_____
_____
_____

PRAISE/WORSHIP

_____
_____
_____
_____
_____
_____

WISDOM/STUDY

_____
_____
_____
_____
_____
_____

PRAYER

_____
_____
_____
_____
_____
_____

JOURNAL

God_____

Gratitude

_____
_____
_____
_____
_____
_____

Praise/Worship

_____
_____
_____
_____
_____
_____

Wisdom/study

_____
_____
_____
_____
_____

Prayer

_____
_____
_____
_____
_____
_____

JOURNAL

God_____

Gratitude

_____
_____
_____
_____
_____
_____

Praise/Worship

_____
_____
_____
_____
_____
_____

Wisdom/study

_____
_____
_____
_____
_____
_____

Prayer

_____
_____
_____
_____
_____
_____

Journal

God_____

Gratitude

_____
_____
_____
_____
_____
_____

Praise/Worship

_____
_____
_____
_____
_____
_____

Wisdom/study

_____
_____
_____
_____
_____
_____

Prayer

_____
_____
_____
_____
_____
_____

Journal

God_____

GRATITUDE

_____
_____
_____
_____
_____
_____

PRAISE/WORSHIP

_____
_____
_____
_____
_____
_____

WISDOM/STUDY

_____
_____
_____
_____
_____
_____

PRAYER

_____
_____
_____
_____
_____
_____

Journal

God_____

Gratitude

_____

_____

_____

_____

_____

_____

Praise/Worship

_____

_____

_____

_____

_____

Wisdom/study

_____

_____

_____

_____

_____

Prayer

_____

_____

_____

_____

_____

Journal

God_____

Gratitude

_____
_____
_____
_____
_____
_____

Praise/Worship

_____
_____
_____
_____
_____
_____

Wisdom/study

_____
_____
_____
_____
_____
_____

Prayer

_____
_____
_____
_____
_____
_____

Journal

More Devotionals

Want the Christian Writers' Collection? How about for free? As a member of the launch team (also called advance reader team), you'll get a digital copy before release. All we ask is that you leave an honest review when the next book launches.

Join at **read.ChristWriters.com**

More Devotional Works by Michael Lacey

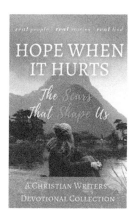

Hope When it Hurts: The Scars that Shape Us (A Christian Writers' Devotional Collection)

It's easy to lose hope, especially in today's world. Through times like these, we all need to be reminded of the *hope of Jesus!*

Hope for the Moment is a collection of what we're calling **Devotional Stories**, *real stories* by *real people* about a *real God*. There are some heavy moments, but in every story, hope is found and God is glorified. These serve to remind of God's *faithfulness* and *goodness*.

While most of the Christian writers in this collection are women, it can serve to encourage *anyone* of *any age*. Writers from around the world have contributed to this collaboration. We celebrate the international feel and have retained author styles.

May the real stories from these real people reflect the real God and **add HOPE to your season.** ***There is hope,*** a *living hope* in Jesus, one that *does not disappoint.*

*Half of the proceeds go to support Star of Hope.

As We Fight: A Weekly Guide Through the
Warfare of Worship

Relevant and Timely Encouragements! (now
comes with FREE Audiobook!)

As your church service approaches the same time
every week, **are you struggling to make
time** for spiritual preparation?

Does worship sometimes feel more like a **task
than an expression?**

Do you often feel **alone in your pursuits as a leader or
worshiper?**

This *well organized and timely book* delivers tried and tested wisdom that
will strengthen your leadership and encourage your team. It will save you
time with its succinct, season-specific devotionals in ONE easy-to-access
place.

This book contains affiliate links. Babies gotta eat!

Also, if you're into fiction, check out some of Michael's writings at:

fiction.MichaelLacey.me

You Must be a Writer...

Have you written a book? After going through this journal, you basically have!

As a person striving after God's heart, I invite you to join our next Christian Writers' Collection. Whether you've published or not, this is open to you.

Go to **ChristWriters.com** for more information.

We also have a Facebook Group,
Christian Writers' Collections at
facebook.com/groups/christiancollections

If you have ANY self-publishing needs, contact
michael@michaellacey.me with StoryBuildsCreative.com

Last Request!

If this journal has helped you in any way, *please leave an honest review on whatever book buying platform/site you use.* This will help get these life-changing books into more hands!

Notes

1 | God's Goodness

1. Goodness Of God: CCLI #7117726 | Ed Cash and Jenn Johnson: © 2018

8 | God's Sovereignty

1. Whole Heart (Hold Me Now); CCLI #7122452 | Aodhan King and Joel Houston; © 2018 | Freedom, Grace, Healing, God's Love, Praise

15 | God Behind the Scenes

1. Way Maker; CCLI #7115744 | Osinachi Kalu Okoro Egbu; © 2016

22 | God My Warrior King

1. Surrounded (Fight My Battles); CCLI #7098758; Elyssa Smith; © 2017 UR Creative (BMI) (adm. at CapitolCMGPublishing.com)
2. Raise A Hallelujah; CCLI #7119315 | Jake Stevens, Jonathan Helser, Melissa Helser, and Molly Skaggs; © Bethel

Made in the USA
Coppell, TX
30 July 2021